Here is the Which Way crew who has been chosen to join you on your Arkansas adventure:

CHIP has brought a fishing rod on this trip. He hopes to catch a buffalofish on the Buffalo National River.

Rita Mapp is an adventurer with a love of travel. She can't wait to go hiking and climbing in the Ozark Mountains.

Table of Contents

WHO is heading for the WHICH WAY HALL OF FAME?

WHAT will be in the WHICH WAY MUSEUM?

WHERE will the WHICH WAY SUPERMAX MOVIE be filmed?

Spa Searching

The crew begins its Arkansas adventure in the town of Hot Springs. This town nearly surrounds a national park with the same name. Hot Springs National Park, the smallest in the United States, is named for the forty-seven hot springs that produce nearly a million gallons of warm, bubbling water every day.

Naturally, after his long trip to the Natural State, Hugh Tern would like to relax in a bubbling bath. So the crew heads for Bathhouse Row in the heart of the park. These old bathhouses, or spas, are open for tours. It is still possible to "take the waters," too.

Before Hugh can jump in, he will need to find the rest of the crew. See if you can spot Hugh and the others. Then spring over to the bottom of page 3 for a clue.

Did you find all five crew members?
Which two are farthest apart?

If Hugh and CHIP are farthest apart,
cross off the composer.

If Baskerville and Professor Pfeffer are,
cross off the president.

If CHIP and Rita are,
cross off the pitcher.

If Rita and Professor Pfeffer are,
cross off the civil-rights leader.

Turn to page 28 and do what the clue says.

Hidden Gems

After relaxing in Hot Springs, the crew returns to the road. Hugh drives southwest to Murfreesboro. The next stop is scenic Crater of Diamonds State Park. This is the only active diamond mine in North America. Since 1906, more than 70,000 diamonds have been dug up here. The largest, nicknamed "Uncle Sam," weighed more than forty carats. It is worth about $250,000!

In a typical year, around 600 diamonds are found here. Best of all, visitors are allowed to keep the ones they find. So with Baskerville leading the way, the crew starts digging. As the crew members look for diamonds, you have your own searching to do. Find all the items hidden in this scene. Then unearth a clue on the bottom of page 5.

Y0-AES-477

camera

candle

baton

teapot

string

jar

flower

Did you find every object?
One of them is hidden twice.
Write its name here:

_____

Now turn to page 28 and cross off the
famous person whose name also
contains all of those letters.

5

Name That Town

The crew heads south to Interstate 30 and then southwest to the Texas border. Your next stop is Texarkana, which is actually two towns—one is in Texas and the other is in Arkansas. State Line Avenue divides the two towns and runs right to the post office.

According to Professor Pfeffer, Texarkana is only one of many unusual Arkansas town names. One town, called Tomato, was named by one of its young citizens. Another was named because the directions on the town application form said, "Write in ink," so the townspeople did. The town is still known as Ink. Another town name, Crossroads or Cross Roads, appears seven times in Arkansas!

There is only one "Cross Roads" and lots of other hidden town names in this word search. The words are hidden up, down, across, backwards, and diagonally. (Don't forget to write in Ink!) Then pick up a clue on the bottom of the page.

ARKANSAS TOWNS

Bee Branch
Cross Roads
Dogpatch
Economy
Fifty Six
Greasy Corner
Ink
Nimrod
Okay
Ozone
Pea Ridge
Peel
Possum Grape
Romance
Seaton Dump
Stamps
Success
Texarkana
Tomato
Twist
"Y" City

G E P A R G M U S S O P
H R F I F T Y S I X T Y
C R E G D I R A E P M B
T D O A P E E L M O A E
A O T M S Y H U N S N E
P R A E A Y D O U O A B
G M M K C N C C Z P K R
O I O I O E C O R E R A
D N T T S E I E R K A N
D Y A T S I W T E N X C
N E T S T A M P S I E H
S D A O R S S O R C T R

Did you circle all the towns? Write the leftover letters, in order
from left to right and top to bottom, in the spaces below.

— — — — —   — — — — — — —

Now turn to page 28 and cross this famous
Arkansan off your list.

7

Courtroom Quiz

The Which Way crew members head north on Route 71. After a long drive, they arrive in Fort Smith. In the 1800s, this was the site of a rugged frontier town. Bandits, robbers, and gamblers made themselves at home and ruled until Isaac Parker arrived in 1875. Judge Parker presided strictly over the federal district court at Fort Smith, restoring law and order. The people of Fort Smith were so thankful that they have preserved his courtroom to this day. It is called the Fort Smith National Historic Site.

The crew arrives in Judge Parker's courtroom at the same time as a group of Arkansas kids on a class trip. The kids think they are telling the truth about their state, but some are making mistakes. Can you figure out how many are guilty of false statements? After you do, judge what to do on the bottom of page 9.

Farmers often flood their fields to help the rice grow.

The Plum Bayou people built the Toltec Mounds.

The end of Whitaker Point Trail is 700 feet above the Buffalo River Valley.

WHICH WAY USA?
STATE MAP

Don't Forget Your Map!
All of the information you need is on the *back* of your Arkansas map.

Turn to page 28 and cross off one person.

Garden Tangle

The crew continues north on Highway 71 and then takes Route 62 east to Eureka Springs. This quaint Victorian city and former artists' colony has been nicknamed "The Switzerland of the Ozarks." Its steep streets are lined with historic buildings. Some have unusual entrances because of the steepness of the hills: they may be entered from the top floor, bottom floor, or sometimes in between.

One of the town's most popular stops is the Blue Springs Heritage Center. The center is lined with shrubs, trees, pools, and streams. The water comes from Blue Spring, which puts out around 38 million gallons of water daily.

With Rita in the lead, the crew walks along the paths past gazebos, bridges, and bushes. Soon Baskerville runs off to chase a hummingbird. Before long, the Which Way hound is lost. Can you help Baskerville find a path back to the rest of the crew? After you do, stroll over to the bottom of page 11.

Did you find the way from Baskerville to the rest of the crew? Now write the letters along the correct path from *last* to *first*:

___ ___ ___ ___ ___ ___ ___

Use this clue to cross one final Arkansas citizen off the list on page 28.

Get On Board!

With Baskerville back, the crew decides to stick together. They want to stay in Eureka Springs to tour the beautiful town, but everyone wants to see different sites. "Eureka!" exclaims Professor Pfeffer as he examines a brochure. "Let's take the trolley and see them all—together!"

They hop on one of Eureka Springs's colorful trolleys. The town's turn-of-the-century-looking trolleys are the perfect way to check out some of the historic sites. And there are a lot of them—the entire downtown is listed on the National Register of Historic Places. As the gang views some of the more than one hundred stops around town, you have a clue to track down.

Use the scene to complete the picture code. Then journey to the bottom of page 13.

Did you crack the code?
Now turn to page 29. Write
your first four code words
in the correct spaces
on that page.

Fishing for Clues

The crew leaves Eureka Springs and drives southeast. Hugh and CHIP are eager to see the Buffalo National River. This beautiful river flows nearly 150 miles through the Ozarks. It was the nation's first river to be protected by federal law. The river is a popular spot for canoeing and fishing.

The crew piles into a pair of canoes and glides along the river. Hugh and CHIP have brought their fishing rods. They hope to catch some of the fish found in the freshwaters of Arkansas. Meanwhile, you need to take the bait, too. See if you can land the names of sixteen fish in the grid on page 15. Fit in only those words that are in all capital letters. Then cast your eyes on the box at the bottom of the page.

Fish

CARP

BREAM

BROWN Trout

PERCH

WHITE Bass

CATFISH

CRAPPIE

LEOPARD Darter

PANFISH

RAINBOW Trout

SPOTTED Bass

STRIPED Bass

WALLEYE

LARGEMOUTH Bass

SMALLMOUTH Bass

BUFFALOFISH

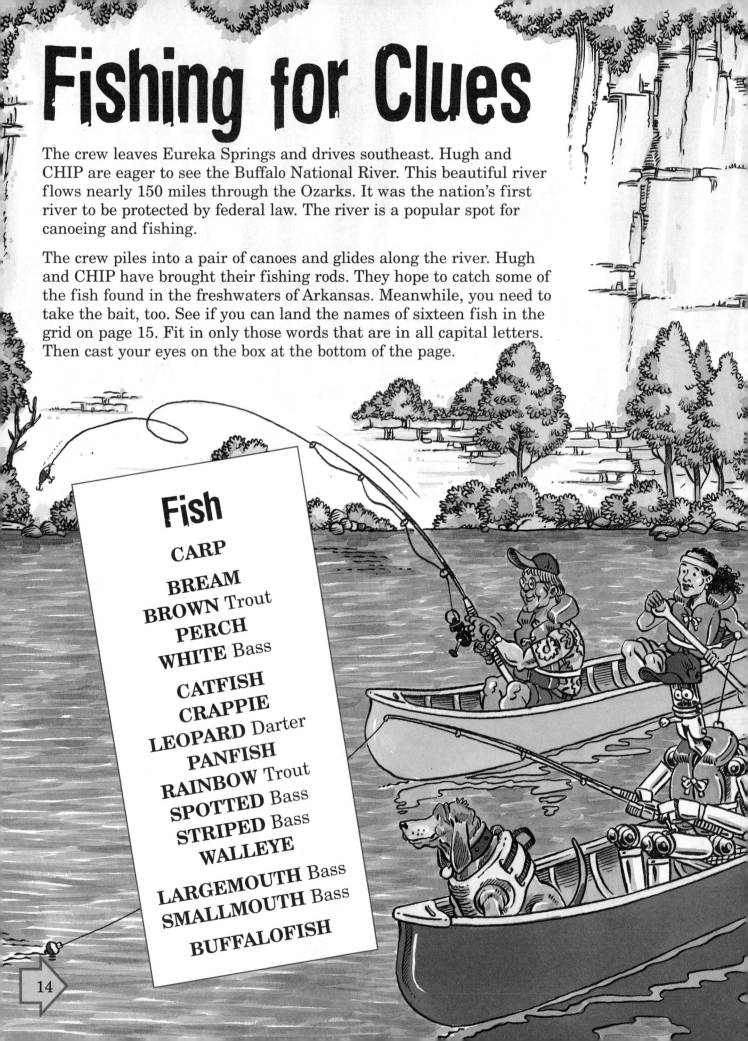

Did you find a place for all the fish? Now use the letters in the colored boxes. Write each set of letters, in order from top to bottom, on the lines below.

Yellow boxes: _____

Pink boxes: _____

Blue boxes: _____

Now turn to page 29 and write these words in the correct spaces.

Ozark Overlook

The crew takes scenic Route 7 into the Ozark National Forest. Rita wants to do some hiking and rock-climbing along the Ozark Highlands Trail, one of the most spectacular trails in the United States. The 165-mile-long trail stretches from Lake Fort Smith State Park to the Buffalo National River.

Rita leads the crew along a rocky stretch on the steep trail. The gang stops to rest at a stunning overlook. As the crew members enjoy the view, you have some work to do! The rock wall where they are resting has words that have something to do with Arkansas. Use the clues to cross off as many words as you can. When you have finished knocking out words, view a clue on the bottom of page 17.

CLUES

1. Cross out any states that border Arkansas.

2. Remove the state instrument.

3. Knock out the city where Interstates 40 and 30 meet.

4. Cross out any major Arkansas lakes.

5. Delete the place that's been a college town since 1871.

6. Knock out any rejected spellings of *Arkansas.*

WHICH WAY USA?

STATE MAP

Don't Forget Your Map!
All of the information you need
is on your Arkansas map.

FROM   FAYETTEVILLE   MILLWOOD   FIDDLE

OKLAHOMA   TENNESSEE   LOUISIANA   THE

ARKENSA   LITTLE ROCK   ARKANSOA   WORD

TEXAS   BULL SHOALS   ARKANCAS   GREERS FERRY

ARKANSAS   BEAVER

Did you find all the answers?
Now turn to page 29 and write
the words you did *not* cross off,
in order from top to bottom,
in the correct spaces.

Toad the Line

Hugh drives down I-40 heading east until the crew reaches the town of Conway. Everyone wants to see the annual Toad Suck Daze Festival. The name "Toad Suck" dates back to the time when steamboats traveled the Arkansas River. The festival is filled with old and new ways to celebrate. Among the fun activities are arts, crafts, a carnival, a baby crawl, and pony rides. There is also a "toadally" cool toad-jumping contest where the competitors try to urge their toads across the finish line without touching them.

In today's race, only four of the toads made it to the finish line. Use the clues below to find the toads that finished first, second, third, and fourth. Then hop over to the bottom of page 19.

DELETE 1

NEXT 2

ABOVE 3

IN 4

CLUES

1. Toad #6 finished right after toad #7.

2. Toad #5 froze and never did move.

3. An odd-numbered toad came in 3rd, two hops behind the winner.

4. After a quick start, toad #1 stopped, turned around, and hopped off the course.

5. Toad #2 and toad #3 quit the race to hunt for flies.

6. Although the winning toad and toad #8 were neck and neck, toad #8 was beaten by a half hop.

DRAWING 5

BELOW 6

PICTURE 7

THE 8

Did you figure out the order of the four who finished the race?
Write that information here:

Toad #_____   Toad #_____   Toad #_____   Toad #_____
   1st   2nd   3rd   4th

Now write the words that appear on their lanes,
in the order of finish.

_____   _____   _____   _____

Turn to page 29 and write these four words in the correct spaces.

Little Rock Walk

The crew leaves the toads behind and hops down I-40 to Little Rock. The state's capital city sits on a bluff overlooking the Arkansas River. The city is filled with many historical sites, and Professor Pfeffer wants to see them all.

Hugh drives down Seventh Street and parks near the Quapaw Quarter. This neighborhood contains most of the city's oldest buildings. Many homes from the 1800s have been carefully restored.

While the crew tours the quaint Quapaw Quarter, you have your own quizzical quest to quickly complete. Circle the letter of the correct answer to each question to qualify for a clue. Then continue your quest on the bottom of page 21.

Don't Forget Your Map!
All of the information you need is
on your Arkansas map.

1. What is the state tree of Arkansas?

   b. pine   **d. poplar**   **f. peach**

2. Where is the National Wild Turkey Calling Contest held?

   a. Yellville   **e. Butcher's Holler**
   r. Gobbler

3. In what year did Arkansas become the 25th state?

   s. 1803   **t. 1836**   **w. 1863**

4. What is the highest point in Arkansas?

   i. Whitaker Point   **s. Mountain View**
   t. Magazine Mountain

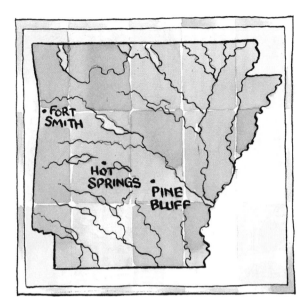

5. What is the fifth-most-populous city in Arkansas?

c. Fort Smith   **l. Jonesboro**
n. Hot Springs

6. Which Arkansas mountain has an International Butterfly Festival?

d. Whitaker Point
e. Mount Magazine
g. Mount McKinley

7. Which is a state nickname of Arkansas?

m. The Diamond State
p. The Pine State
s. The Natural State

8. Who started the first permanent European settlement in what is now the state of Arkansas?

h. Robert Cavelier   **i. Henri de Tonti**
l. Hernando de Soto

9. What is the Arkansas state beverage?

a. apple cider   **n. iced tea**
t. milk

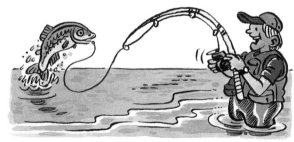

10. About how large was the brown trout caught by Rip Collins in 1992?

e. 40 pounds   **s. 45 pounds**
y. 47 pounds

Have you found all the answers? Now write the letters you circled in the spaces below.

— — — — —   — — — —

Turn to page 30 and cross off this famous Arkansas place.

SANDY STEPS

The crew members leave Little Rock and drive northeast on Route 67. After 90 miles or so, they roll into the town of Newport. Nearby Jacksonport State Park is the site of the annual Portfest Rollin' on the River Festival. The river is the White River and the festival is filled with riverside events. There are spectacular fireworks and a catfish-cooking contest.

The crew decides to check out some kids building sand castles in the park. Hugh and Baskerville can't resist getting into the act. Professor Pfeffer snaps a series of pictures of their work. See if you can put the pictures in order from first to last. Then dig up a clue on the bottom of page 23.

Did you put the pictures in order? Now write the letters from the pictures, in the same order, to complete the message.

Cross off the

_____ and ___ ___ ___ ___ ___ ___.

Use the clue to cross out a pair of famous places on page 30.

Guppy Love

The crew heads southwest to Lonoke. This is the heart of Arkansas's fish-farming industry. In fact, Lonoke claims to be the "Minnow Capital of the World." The Joe Hogan State Fish Hatchery here is one of the largest fish hatcheries in the world.

The crew decides to visit a fish farm. They discover that the fish are raised in large pools that look like ponds. As the crew stares into the clear blue water, schools of fish swim about. CHIP watches as the fish swim by, but they are moving so fast that it is hard to keep track of them all. Help him by counting the number of fish in the picture. When you have your total, pick up a fishy clue on the bottom of page 25.

Did you figure out how many fish are in the pool?

If there are fewer than 60,
cross off the Ozark Folk Center.

If there are exactly 60,
cross off Hot Springs National Park.

If there are more than 60,
cross off the Old State House.

Now turn to page 30 and use this clue.

Farm Functions

Your Arkansas adventure is nearly finished. The crew makes one final stop in Stuttgart. The town was named for the city in Germany because many Germans settled here. The Museum of the Arkansas Grand Prairie preserves the traditions and tools of the rice farmers who worked here from the 1880s until 1921. There are buildings from that period and both indoor and outdoor displays. The crew wanders through the museum trying to guess what some of the farm tools were used for.

Meanwhile, you have one last bit of guesswork, too. Plow your way clockwise around the crop field by filling in the answers in the grid on page 27. The last letter of the first answer becomes the first letter of the second answer. Keep going until you get back to the first square again. Then harvest a clue at the bottom of the page.

Clues

1. Diamonds were discovered near here in 1906.
2. Arkansas's lowest point lies along this river.
3. This is one of the state's major rivers.
4. The diamond is Arkansas's _____

   _____.
5. These are the first four letters of two of Arkansas's state neighbors.

   _____
6. The honeybee is Arkansas's _____

   _____.
7. This city is found on the Arkansas-Texas border, the reason for its unusual name.
8. Arkansas's state flower is the _____.

Don't Forget Your Map!
All the answers can be found
on your Arkansas map.

WHICH WAY USA?

STATE MAP

Did you find all the answers? Starting at the top row of the square and going *counterclockwise*, write the letters from the shaded boxes in the spaces below.

Cross off the

— — — —   — — — — — —.

Now turn to page 30 and eliminate this Arkansas location.

Who?

Which famous person from Arkansas is going into the Which Way Hall of Fame? To find out, solve the puzzles on pages 2 through 11. Each puzzle will help you eliminate one person. When there is only one choice left, he or she will be the hall-of-famer!

General Douglas MacArthur
Little Rock native who commanded the Allied Forces in the Southwest Pacific during World War II

Jay Hanna "Dizzy" Dean
Star pitcher for the St. Louis Cardinals and member of the National Baseball Hall of Fame

Hattie Ophelia Wyatt Caraway
First woman elected to the U.S. Senate and the first to head a Senate committee

William Jefferson Clinton
Born in Hope, Arkansas's youngest governor and the 42nd U.S. president

William Grant Still
Composer and the first African American to conduct an American symphony orchestra

Daisy Gatson Bates
Civil-rights leader who fought to integrate Arkansas's schools and cofounder of the *Arkansas State Press*

The person going into the Hall of Fame is:

What?

One thing from Arkansas has been selected to be exhibited in the Which Way Museum. To find out what it is, solve the puzzles on pages 12 through 19. Fill in the answers. Then follow the directions of the answer words. You will have to solve all of the puzzles to determine what will go into the Which Way Museum.

Pages 12-13: _ _ _ _ _ _ _ _ _ _ _ _ _ _ _ _

Pages 14-15: _ _ _ _ _ _ _ _ _ _ _ _ _ _

Pages 16-17: _ _ _ _ _ _ _ _ _ _ _ " _ _ _ _ _ _ _ "
              1   2   3   4 5   6

Pages 18-19: _ _ _ _ _ _ _ _ _ _ _ _ _ _ _ _ _.
             7 8   9 10 11   12   13   14

Now use the numberd letters above to complete the code below.

The item going into the Which Way Museum is:

$\overline{5}$ $\overline{3}\ \overline{10}\ \overline{5}\ \overline{2}\ \overline{14}\ \overline{7}\ \overline{3}$ $\overline{1}\ \overline{12}\ \overline{14}\ \overline{2}$ $\overline{11}\ \overline{12}\ \overline{5}\ \overline{8}\ \overline{13}\ \overline{12}$ $\overline{14}\ \overline{1}$

$\overline{3}\ \overline{10}\ \overline{5}\ \overline{2}\ \overline{14}\ \overline{7}\ \overline{3}\ \overline{6}$ $\overline{6}\ \overline{8}\ \overline{5}\ \overline{8}\ \overline{13}$ $\overline{9}\ \overline{5}\ \overline{12}\ \overline{4}$

Where?

One landmark from Arkansas is to be featured in the Which Way Supermax Movie. To find out where the Which Way cameras are going, solve the puzzles on pages 20 through 27. Each puzzle will help you cross off one or more of the famous places. When you finish, the remaining landmark will be the answer.

Hot Springs National Park
The smallest national park in the U.S., featuring 47 natural hot springs and a row of beautiful old bathhouses

Petit Jean State Park
Arkansas's first state park and one of its loveliest, with 20 miles of hiking trails and a Native American rock shelter

Blanchard Springs Caverns
Ozark National Forest site known for its rooms of sparkling flowstone and towering columns

The Ozark Folk Center
A living museum that preserves the arts, crafts, music, and culture of early Ozark Mountain settlers

The Old State House
The state's first capitol building, opened in 1836, now a state history museum

Pea Ridge National Military Park
Site of the first Civil War battle in the state and the largest battle west of the Mississippi River

The famous place is:

All the answers for your
Which Way adventure
are on the next two
pages. Do not go

unless you need help
with a puzzle. If you
don't need help,

before you look at
the answers.

You can use the rest of
this page to work out
your puzzles. If you need
a little extra space,

your pencil here. After
you're done, make a

back to the page you
were working on.

ANSWERS

Pages 2-3: Spa Searching

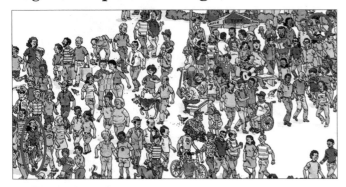

CHIP and Rita are farthest apart. On page 28, cross off pitcher Dizzy Dean.

Pages 4-5: Hidden Gems

The string is hidden twice. On page 28, cross off William Grant Still, whose name contains all the letters in STRING.

Pages 6-7: Name That Town

```
G E P A R G M U S S O P
H R F I F T Y S I X T Y
C R E G D I R A E P M B
T D O A P E E L M O A E
A O T M S Y H U N S N E
P R A E A Y D O U O K B
G M M K C N C C Z P E R
O I O I O E C O R E K A
D N T T S E I E R K R N
D Y A T S I W T E N X C
N E T S T A M P S I E H
S D A O R S S O R C T R
```

The leftover letters spell THE PRESIDENT. Cross off William Clinton on page 28.

Pages 8-9: Courtroom Quiz

The statements about Cedar Falls, Ozark National Forest, Toltec Mounds, and Hot Springs are false. Since there are four false statements, cross off Hattie Caraway on page 28.

Pages 10-11: Garden Tangle

From last to first, the letters along the path spell GENERAL. Cross off General Douglas MacArthur on page 28.

Pages 12-13: Get on Board!

"S H A D E   I N   E A C H   S H A P E"

I S   Y O U R   F I R S T   C L U E .

Write the clue in the spaces on page 29.

Pages 14-15: Fishing for Clues

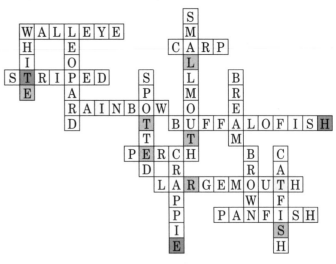

The letters from the shaded boxes spell WITH THE LETTERS. Write these words on page 29.